T3-BEA-546

Windows *on the* Master

Windows *on the* Master

Charles C. Wise, Jr.

Abingdon Press   (♪)   NASHVILLE • NEW YORK

WINDOWS ON THE MASTER

Copyright © 1968 by Abingdon Press

Library of Congress Catalog Card Number: 68-25365

SET UP, PRINTED, AND BOUND BY THE
PARTHENON PRESS, AT NASHVILLE,
TENNESSEE, UNITED STATES OF AMERICA

To the memory of my son

Charles Conrad Wise III ("Terry")
1946-1967

Poet, painter, and singing actor.
We shall always be grateful for the
beauty, zest, and love revealed in
and through him.

About This Book

The interest aroused by *Windows on the Passion* has made this volume possible.

Dramatic moments in the public life of Jesus are viewed through the eyes of persons directly involved. Their reports provide a series of picture windows on the ministry of our Lord.

Subjects discussed encompass Jesus' relations with his family, with sinners, with women—both good and bad, and with foreigners. Some contemporary social customs are clarified. Style and format are consistent with the preceding volume.

Encouragement and advice have been given by the Reverend Cletus and Betty Hirschy, Dr. Floy S. Hyde of Hartwick College, and Mr. Charles H. Schafer. Mrs. Nini Horn has performed miracles of intuition with the manuscript.

Again I caution the reader that my characters

are subject to human error and bias, and that he should check the accounts they give here with his own Bible. A page at the back of the book shows the scriptural references for each section. I hope to stimulate thought, particularly where you disagree.

Before the reader begins, may I suggest the following prayer of preparation:

> O Lord, mop off our minds
> that we may see thee clear,
> undistorted by the dusts of time
> or the shimmering cobwebs
> of our own concerns.
>
> Amen.

July 4, 1968
Charles C. Wise, Jr.
Washington, D. C.

Contents

Contents

I

Temple Talk

Jesus in the Temple at the age of twelve, as recalled by Caiaphas, High Priest at Jerusalem.

Temple Talk

*A*s they brought the prisoner
into the room,
I, Caiaphas,
High Priest of the Temple
of the Most High God
at Jerusalem,
recognized him—
and remembered.

So that child is the Nazarene.
It must have been about twenty years ago.
Annas—my new father-in-law,
although he is barely ten years older than I—
was High Priest at the time.
Traditionally the office was for life,
but since the Romans came
the appointment has been shuffled around
to suit their policy and convenience.
I am fortunate to have lasted fifteen years.
Believe me, it takes some doing
to keep the Romans satisfied
and the country on an even keel.
My post is no sinecure.

*A*s one of the Elders,
I sat often in the Temple Court,
discussing problems, giving advice,
and mending organizational fences.
It was Passover time,
and many visitors
had crowded into the city.
He came in and looked around
as if he were seeking someone.
He was a handsome lad,
self-possessed and seeming anything but shy,
but politely refraining
from interrupting our deliberations
by speaking before he was spoken to.
Even then, he gave promise
of the distinguished personality
he has since become.

I was attracted to him,
and spoke to set him at ease.
"What is the matter, Son,
are you lost?"
He flashed a bright grin
and replied promptly,
"Reverend Sir,
no good Jew
can be lost
if he is in the Temple

14

of the Most High God.
But, truth to tell,
I have become separated
from my parents.
We were to have started
back to our home at Hyrcania
early yesterday.
I stopped to watch
an Egyptian juggler
and, before I noticed,
they had gone,
and I could not find them.
They told me if I were lost
to go straight to the Temple.
When I am missed
they will surely seek me here.
And I shall wait right here.
I was in this crowd
most of yesterday afternoon.
Last night I slept on a bench
in the Outer Court.
They will surely come for me today."

"Well," I said to him,
"You are quite a talker.
How old are you?"
"Sir," he answered,
"I am twelve years old."
He was a keen, intelligent,

and pleasant lad.
I found conversing with him
much more interesting
than following the dull discussion
going on among the Elders
as to how many household objects
could successively be left,
to maintain the fiction home was there,
before there was a violation
of the law forbidding Sabbath journeys
of more than the stated distance from one's home.
I feared the old rule of seven times
was about to be invoked again.

I spoke to the boy,
"Is this your first trip to the city?
How do you like Jerusalem?"
"Sir, it is big, busy,
noisy, and exciting.
This Temple must be
the finest building in the world.
I am very glad I could come.
But one thing puzzles me.
We came here for Passover
because this is the House of God
and he is here.
But I do not feel any different here,
and most of the people who live here with him

16

don't act as nice as those who live elsewhere.
Why aren't all people kind and good?
And why don't they get better
when they live closer to God?"

Now this was a poser
I was in no hurry to answer.
While I was hesitating
old Eleazer,
who had been listening,
undertook to explain to him
about the Garden of Eden
and the origin of sin.
The boy was only half satisfied.
"But God made everything,
and after each day's work
he inspected the job
and pronounced it 'good.'
Now if he made the serpent
and inspected it,
how could it be evil
or work against God?
I'll bet my father
wouldn't let a mistake like that
get past his inspection."

*E*leazar saw a chance
to change the subject

and get out of deep water:
"Who is your father,
and what does he do?"
"My father is Joseph ben Heli,
master carpenter of Hyrcania.
He builds buildings
and makes furniture.
I think he must be
the best carpenter in the world;
he does such beautiful work.
When he and Mother
came up for Passover,
they brought me with them
because I wanted very much
to see the Temple.
Next year I celebrate
my Bar Mitzvah*
and take my place
as a Son of the Law.
I wish to learn all I can
about what it means.
Who are you,
and what do you do?
Do you just sit here and talk all day?
What about?"

* Literally, "Son of the Commandment"—one who has reached the age of responsibility before the Law. Although not celebrated in the modern sense or under that name prior to the fourteenth century, some kind of rites to recognize coming of age probably were observed.

*E*leazar and I introduced ourselves
and told him we were Elders of the People,
Members of the Sanhedrin,
and sat in the Women's Court
to decide law cases,
give advice on personal and family problems,
and look for the Messiah.

He was very interested
and asked, "What will he be like?
How will you recognize him?
Will he throw the Romans out?"

We told him of some of the prophecies:
that many looked for a warrior king,
and that some looked for two Messiahs,
one a priest and the other a king.
However, others wondered if Isaiah's poems
about a suffering servant of the Lord
might not suggest a different Messiah
than most expected.
By this time, the others had—
    one by one—
dropped their dry discussion of the Law
and clustered around us,
completely absorbed in our discussion.
One suggested that the Messiah
would, of course, be descended from David
and would be born in Bethlehem.

The boy became quiet excited.
"I have been told
that I was born in Bethlehem—
although I don't remember anything about it.
And I know we are of the House of David,
and my father may be descended from him.
Do you think I may be the Messiah?"

"Well," I answered,
"It's a little early
for us to tell.
But I expect that when he comes
he will be a good, polite,
and intelligent boy
a lot like you.
What are you going to be
when you grow up?"

The boy smiled.
"If I turn out not to be the Messiah,
I shall be a good carpenter—
    like my father.
Already I do good work
and help him make things.
He often takes me with him
and lets me hand him tools.
He says I am a good assistant.
But maybe I shall be a preacher, too;

20

I like to talk.
Now, if I am the Messiah,
I shall need to know
a lot of things about our religion.
Perhaps you learned men
know the answers to my questions
and will instruct me.
What is God like?"

We were a little slow in answering;
how do you explain God to a child
when he is not too clear to you?
But some suggested: Creator, Good, Holy,
All-powerful, All-knowing, Loving,
Just-in-judgment, Merciful.
It was all very obscure to the boy,
and he said so.
"It is very difficult to understand.
I think of God as a father.
He must be something
like my father Joseph.
Joseph is good, and kind to me.
He makes beautiful things
for people to use and enjoy.
I shall think of God
as my Heavenly Father."
We were all silent a moment—
thinking.

*T*hen the boy asked,
"Which is the greatest Psalm?"
Here there was less trouble.
While one or two had other favorites,
there was general agreement
that David's *Shepherd Psalm*,
known by heart to all,
which has inspired and comforted
so many in their trouble,
was preeminent.
Jesus thought so too.
"Yes, a good shepherd's
care for his sheep
is like the firm kindness
of a father's love.
I think that is how
God feels toward us."

"It must be nice," he went on,
"spending your days here—
    as you do—
so close to God,
and doing nothing
but thinking and talking
about his Word and Will.
Have you all seen God?"
We each admitted
that we never had.
"Why? Isn't he here?

22

I thought that he stayed
in the Temple?
Where does God live?
Is it in Heaven, then?"

He paused for a moment,
then asked, "Where is Heaven?
Somewhere up in the sky?
What is it like?
Does God live there
most of the time?
What is there in Heaven
for God and the angels to stand on?
If he lives there,
how can he dwell in the Temple?
Do we go there to be with him
after we die?"

At this point,
all the others
politely deferred to my status
as the High Priest's son-in-law.
So I tried to reply
and told him that God
is not an idol made by hands,
nor yet a creature with a body,
but that God is spirit
and cannot be seen.

23

Jesus objected,
"That isn't what my father—
  Joseph—
has told me.
Didn't Moses see God
  on the mountain?
Didn't Isaiah see God
  in this temple?
Didn't Ezekiel see God
  in distant Babylon?"

I explained that these
and other prophets
had had deep, inner
personal experiences
of the presence of God
that had changed their lives,
and that they had sought
to tell us about them
as best they could
  in words.
These experiences were real.
They had sensed his nearness,
and their minds had received his Word,
but they had not seen or heard
with the outer eye and ear.
I reminded him of Elijah;
God's Word was not in the storm,
but in the still, small voice.

24

As spirit,
God was everywhere—
    simultaneously—
and he had made his presence felt
to the prophets,
wherever they were.

The boy bubbled with questions.
"Is this simultaneous everywhere
what we call Heaven?
If God is everywhere,
what do they mean
by calling this God's House?
Why do we have the Temple?"

I tried to explain that,
while God was everywhere
and while there also was Heaven,
we were his Chosen People,
specially selected by him
and forged into a holy nation
and a kingdom of priests,
for the particular purpose of revealing
his will to the world.
He had made with us
a series of covenants:
we had agreed to be his people,
and he had promised to be our God.

It was only because
we had often been unfaithful
that he had withdrawn
his support from us
and permitted us to fall
under the power of foreign foes.
But because he is merciful
and has never ceased to try
to reestablish contact,
his presence is still with us
and—in some special sense—
dwells behind the veil
in the Holy of Holies,
the inner room in the Temple
behind the Sanctuary.

*J*esus was not satisfied,
"Why is there a veil?
I would tear down anything
that separates me from God.
Why do we keep him
    at a distance?
Why don't we try to live
    in his presence?"

I went far back
into the history of our people.
I recalled how Moses,

26

after he had received from God
the Ten Commandments,
had marshaled the people
at Mount Sinai
to hear God's voice;
how the people
had feared and trembled,
and had said to Moses:

> "You speak to us,
>   and we will hear;
>   but let not God
>   speak to us,
>   lest we die";

how Moses had answered:

> "Do not fear,
>   for God has come to prove you,
>   so that the fear of him
>   may be before your eyes
>   that you may not sin";*

how the people sinned
with the Golden Calf
while Moses was yet on the mountain;
how the Tablets were broken,

* Exodus 20:19, 20.

27

and God's anger was kindled;
how he withdrew from among them,
and would speak to Moses only;
how Moses, when he came down
from talking with the Lord,
had such a glory
shining from his face
that the people feared and fled,
that only Aaron and the leaders
would remain to listen,
and that Moses placed
a veil before his face,
which he removed
only to speak to God
or to speak God's Word
  to the people;
and how God's presence
was so terrible
that even its reflected light
as seen in the face
of his Servant Moses
was more than could be borne
by any except those
prepared by a lifetime of dedication
to risk exposure to it.

While the people of Israel
journeyed in the wilderness,
the Lord dwelt in the Tabernacle,

and when they gained the Promised Land
and Solomon had built the Temple,
the Lord descended upon it
and took up his abode
in the Holy of Holies—
    behind the veil.
While he is here in some special sense,
God no longer speaks to prophets.
He remains remote
and can be approached only once each year—
    on the Day of Atonement—
by the High Priest.
On that day,
dressed in his richest robes
encrusted with jewels,
wearing the Breastplate of Judgment
containing the Twelve Precious Stones
representing the Twelve Tribes,
wrapped in the Sacred Ephod,
and bearing on his head
the Sacred Mitre,
the High Priest—
as representative of the Nation—
enters the Holy of Holies,
asks mercy for the nation's sins,
sprinkles the blood of the sin offering
on the Mercy Seat,
burns incense within the veil,
and pledges the people's promises

to a renewal of the Covenant.
Then—as God's representative—
he emerges to announce
God's gracious forgiveness,
the renewal of the Covenant
for another year,
and any special instructions
that the Lord might have
     for his people.

*T*he youth never missed a word;
he was entirely absorbed
and seemed hardly to breathe.
"What happens," he asked,
"while the High Priest is in there?
How does God talk to him?"
We each said we did not know;
the High Priest was forbidden to tell.
Even though I was his son-in-law,
had often talked with him about his duties,
and was very curious myself about it,
he had never discussed it,
and I had feared to ask.

(Yes, I had often wondered.
I did not tell the boy
how much for years I wondered
whether Annas saw or felt anything

30

when he went beyond the veil.
Was our faith based on a living Presence?
Was there a Force behind the forms?
Was Annas in the Shekinah
and conscious of the Presence
while in the Holy of Holies?
Or was he just a worried old man—
    alone and in the dark—
groping in a closet
for the answers to hard questions?
Well—God help me!—
now I know!
My respect for my father-in-law
has risen a great deal
through the years.
He lasted eight years as High Priest
and is still living.
His three successors—
    my predecessors—
lasted barely a year apiece.
No wonder I seek his advice
and respect his judgment!)

"This idea of the veil,"
said Jesus, "worries me.
Do you suppose Moses wore it
to conceal the fact
that God's splendor faded from his face
after he had been for some time

out of God's presence?
No! He wouldn't do that!
He was a good man.
But there is something dishonest
about a veil.
Veils are worn
to hide what's behind them.
Who is hiding behind
the Temple Veil?
Is God hiding from us,
or did we put it up
to hide from him?
What do you think?"

Old Jerahmeel threw up his hands
in mingled confusion and admiration.
"Such questions!
What a boy!
Maybe yet you will be a prophet!
Or the Messiah, even!
My son, if you get answers
to these hard questions,
you come tell me.
If I believe your answers,
I will recommend you
for appointment as High Priest—
perhaps to succeed Caiaphas there,
who is next in line,

but who ought to be tired of the job
by the time you are ready for it."
(He won't succeed me as High Priest.
But I can't be free
of a vague fear
that he just may have qualified
for a higher office!)

"If God is everywhere,"
said Jesus,
"I am going to look for him
everywhere I am.
And if I find him
and find his will for my life,
I am going to do it.
Moses found him on the mountain.
I like mountains.
Is that a good place to look?"

"But I still don't see,"
the boy persisted,
"why people in the streets
here at Jerusalem
seem so unkind and impolite.
Everyone is in such a hurry,
and pushes us aside
without a single friendly word.
Porters carrying large bundles
even use the Temple courts

as shortcuts to save time
and charge at worshipers,
threatening to run over them
if they don't get out of the way.
Why do they do that
so close to God's presence
if they know he can see them?
They must think they are hidden—
    by the veil—
from his sight."

*P*erhaps they do," said Eleazar,
feeling somewhat uncomfortable
and anxious to change the subject.
"But let me ask you a question.
Who do you think
was the greatest man
in Jewish history?
Abraham? Jacob? Moses?
Elijah? Solomon?
How about your ancestor David?"

The boy smiled.
"I like David," he said.
"I would like it to be he.
He was a big man in every way.
He did great deeds
and united the Nation.

34

He sinned greatly,
but he repented greatly also.
And best of all
he praised God greatly
in the psalms that he wrote.
He was a great man,
and I am proud to be his descendant.
But great as he was,
I think Moses was greater.
God gave him the Law
that even David had to obey,
and it was Moses who asked God
to kill him,
rather than destroy the people
and let him live."
There was smiling agreement.
Only lawyers were present,
and the only thing they can agree on
is that there ought to be a law.

Respected Sirs," the boy asked,
"which is the greatest prophet?"
This stirred up a general disagreement.
Jeremiah, Isaiah, Elijah,
Ezekiel, Daniel: all had
strong proponents present.
And many good arguments
were urged in support.

Finally, Joseph of Arimathea,
the youngest member of our group,
asked our young friend
which was his choice.

The boy showed some hesitation
in replying.
"The scrolls of many of them,"
he said, "are long,
and most I have not read.
Of course, I have heard in synagogue
many great words of each.
So many of them
make God sound angry.
But my father is particularly fond
of Hosea, and has bought me a scroll.
There is one passage that is my favorite.
I have learned it by heart.
Would you like me to say it?
In it, God is saying
how much he loves us.
Have I your permission?
Shall I start now?

'When Israel was a child,
    I loved him,
and I called him out of Egypt
    to be my son.

The more I called them,
    the more they went from me.
They kept sacrificing to the Baals
    and worshiping idols.

Yet it was I who taught Ephraim to walk,
    holding them with my arms;
but they did not know that I healed them
    when they fell and hurt themselves.

I led them with cords of compassion,
    with the bands of love.
I became to them as one who eases
    the bit on their jaws.
I bent down to minister to them
    and gently fed them.'

"Then there's an angry part I don't like,
which I leave out;
and it goes on:

    'How can I give you up, O Ephraim!
    How can I hand you over, O Israel!
        How can I make you like Admah!
        How can I treat you like Zeboiim!
    My heart recoils within me;
    my pity grows warm and tender.

    I will not execute my fierce anger,
    I will not again destroy Ephraim;
        for I am God and not man,

the Holy One in your midst,
and I will not come to destroy.' " *

*L*ovely," said Joseph.
"You recite well.
And the passage is well-chosen.
But I notice that
already the sun is sinking.
If your parents do not appear
before we break up for dinner,
come and be my guest for the night.
I can provide something to eat
and a place to sleep,
and my young bride—
who as yet has no child of her own—
will be delighted to have you as guest."

"Sir," said Jesus,
"I should be honored to accept,
did I not fear my parents
might come during the night
and be frightened at my absence.
I feel I had better be here."

"That won't be necessary,"
said Joseph. "We can leave word

* Hosea 11:1-4; 8-9. (Paraphrase.)

with the watch where you are,
and they will direct your parents
to come to my house.
A slave is on duty at the door
    day and night,
and it will be no trouble
for him to call you."

$\int$ir, you are kind.
If they do not come,
I shall go with you.
But, sirs,
one further question troubles me.
There are so many laws
in the Torah,
and sometimes they even conflict.
Is there one greatest commandment
which at all costs must be obeyed,
when you just can't keep them all?
If there is one basic principle
with which to measure righteousness,
please tell me of it."

I answered him,
"My son, I think there is.
Most of these Elders would tell you—
    and they would say well—
that the Ten Commandments as a unit

are the core of the whole Law,
that they are equally important,
that they must all be obeyed,
and that no one may be singled out
for preeminence.
The Ten Commandments are fundamental
as a guide to conduct.
But I think even more basic
is the law of the Shema
which sets the heart toward God.
Can you recite it?"

"Yes, Sir," the boy replied.

" 'Hear, O Israel:
The Lord our God is one Lord;
and you shall love
the Lord your God
with all your heart,
and with all your soul,
and with all your might.
And these words
which I command you this day
shall be upon your heart;
and you shall teach them diligently
to your children,
and shall talk of them
when you sit in your house,
and when you walk by the way,

and when you lie down,
and when you rise.
And you shall bind them
as a sign upon your hand,
and they shall be
as frontlets between your eyes.
And you shall write them
on the doorposts of your house
and on your gates.' " *

"Good," I told him,
"that was well said."

While the boy was reciting,
a man and woman
came through the Temple gate
immediately behind him.
The woman pointed excitedly at Jesus
and tried to run to him,
but the man held her back—
apparently to learn
what was going on,
or to avoid too sudden an interruption.
I guessed these were the boy's parents
but had not spoken,
when Jesus, who had been thinking,

* Deuteronomy 6:4-9.

looked up at me and said,
"I think you are right.
If I keep my attention on God,
remembering he has his eyes on me,
I get a good start from the right place.
I shall try to learn the will
of my Father in Heaven
and serve him."

"Good," I said.
"But meanwhile here's another father
who looks as if he had a few things
to say to you.
Good evening, my good people.
Is this youth your son?"

*J*esus looked around,
and waved at them.
He seemed to wish
to continue the conversation.
But Joseph ben Heli spoke,
"Yes, Reverend Sir,
this is our son Jesus.
I hope he hasn't been
too much of a nuisance.
I can see he has been
talking his head off."

42

We assured him
that Jesus had been no trouble,
and that we all had enjoyed
our conversation with him.
Old Jerahmeel spoke up,
"Yes, he is a great boy
and a smart youngster;
we enjoyed him.
You should be proud of him.
Perhaps we taught him a few things,
but I for one feel
that I got more from him
than I gave. I hope
that you won't be too hard on him
for getting lost,
and that you will let him
come back and visit us again.
We still have quite a bit to cover
concerning a possible life after death,
and we haven't discussed Gehenna at all."
Joseph smiled his thanks.

While we were talking,
the boy's mother
had grabbed him by one arm—
as if afraid he would disappear again—
and was sounding exactly like a mother,
expressing relief that he was all right

43

by scolding him for the worrying she'd done:
"Son, how could you treat us this way?
We were sure you were in the company
and got a full day's journey from Jerusalem
before we missed you.
By then it was too dark to travel.
I couldn't sleep a wink for worrying
all last night. Today we rushed back
and have been searching anxiously everywhere."

The boy answered her,
being patiently reasonable
as only a youngster can
who is explaining something obvious
to a parent
who just cannot understand,
"Why did you have to search?
Didn't you know I would be right here
in the house of my Heavenly Father?"

*J*oseph of Arimathea spoke up.
"I'm sure you are both tired
and have not taken time
to arrange for a place to stay.
Your son has already agreed
to be my guest. Will you, too,
honor my house this night

with your presence?
This lad of yours is a joy;
he has made every minute of this day a delight.
I wish to learn more about him.
And when he grows up,
I hope he will come to me
whenever he is in Jerusalem.
No matter how crowded the city is,
or how many guests I have,
I promise you I will always have
a place for him."
They thanked him for his kind offer
and accepted it.
Goodbyes and good wishes
were said all around,
and they left.

I had not seen him
in the twenty years since.
But he had made a deep impression
and was not easily forgotten.
I judged from his eyes
that he did not remember me.
So he was the Nazarene.
Yes, I remembered,
Jesus ben Joseph had been his name.
As I looked at him,

all the old liking
that I had felt twenty years before
swept over me.
Here, this would never do.
This man might or might not
be the Messiah.
It really didn't matter
whether he was or not.
It did matter that
a great many people
thought he was.
So he had to die.
With the precarious state
that we were in
in our relations with Rome,
we couldn't afford a Messiah
   right now.

I steeled my heart
to do what I must do
for God and Country.
I wished my young friend,
Saul of Tarsus, were here.
This was a job he would have enjoyed,
and his advice would have been invaluable.
With a grimace of distaste
and a deep sigh of regret,
I began the questioning of Jesus

46

which would bring about his downfall
and would trap him to his death.
I didn't like the assignment,
but I knew I would give it my best
and put on my usual good performance.

II

Next of Kin

The baptism of Jesus of Nazareth as related by his cousin, John the Baptizer, who performed it.

Next of Kin

*W*hen you are in jail,
there is little to do but think.
Over and over again
my mind asks this question:
can Jesus be the long-awaited One,
Israel's Messiah,
and God's Son?

I have known him all my life.
We are cousins through our mothers
and were boys together.
It's hard for me to see him as Messiah
when I have blacked his eye in childish play
and smeared his pretty face with camel dung.
It's hard to believe in greatness
in one's own family;
it seems so unlikely.

*L*ike many preacher's sons,
I was a "bad boy"—
more energetic than evil,
and somewhat defiant

51

because closely criticized by neighbors,
who set for my pious father's son
standards not used to measure against their own.

My parents had been old when I was born,
and vowed in gratitude for their new son
to raise me dedicated to the Lord.
I was ordained a Nazirite for life
before I took a step or spoke a word.
No matter, I have since confirmed the vows.
As such, I could not ever cut my hair,
or drink of wine, or touch a woman.
My hair was full and thick, and curled so tight
before a rain it seemed to stretch my scalp
with pulling.
Perhaps you can imagine how my fellows
would taunt me for my hair, and call me girl.
I learned to fight well in resenting them.

*J*esus came sometimes to visit me
when Aunt Mary could bring him over.
I, some six months older than is he,
was always heavier and stockier,
though not so tall.
I often gave him a pretty rough time.
But he was game—I'll admit that.
He was strong, and very quick,

52

but not so heavily-muscled
or roughly boisterous as I.

Jesus was usually patient and good-humored,
but subject to fierce bursts of anger
in which he suddenly seemed terrible.
My parents couldn't travel to Hyrcania,
so I didn't see him often
or get to know him well.

*W*hen I was seven,
my mother Elizabeth died.
Zacharias, my father, was growing feeble,
and such strength as he had
was needed for service in the Lord's House.
Aunt Mary's growing family
took all her time,
and Uncle Joseph was not well,
so I could not be settled there.
My father finally arranged—
or perhaps it was arranged long before—
for me to live and study with the Essenes
out in the desert, and there I
was raised in their austere community.

Cousin Jesus came to visit a few times.
He was becoming a capable carpenter,
following in Joseph's footsteps,

and a careful and willing workman.
He liked talking with the brothers,
joined us in our ceremonial bathing,
and read many of the sacred scrolls.
He never stayed for long,
and indeed it did not wholly suit him.
He was no anchorite,
but lived in laughter.
He was kind and considerate,
even in argument,
but his irrepressible humor
would at last break forth
in some outrageous story or illustration,
scandalizing the sober Essenes
and—to be honest—myself.
I have laughed but seldom in my life
and never wholly approved of Jesus' laughter.
I never could find fun in sacred things,
or really much in other matters.
He seemed to me too frivolous. But then,
I have no sense of humor.

As one ordained to be a Nazirite,
I wore a woven cloak of camel's hair,
ate only foods held ceremoniously clean—
as locusts, and the honey of the desert
beloved of Samson, also a Nazirite.
My heavy hair, tight gathered at the back,

cascaded in black waves down to my thighs.
My heavy beard merged with my hairy chest
and all the parts of me not hid with hair
the desert sun had blackened.
Such was John the Baptizer, when God called
   him.
I was all black, of face and form and mood,
and most men found me fierce and frightening.

When I was twenty-eight,
and strong as fierce,
as in prayer-watch
I knelt one night alone,
there seemed a voice called to me:
"John, John!"
I answered, "Yes, Lord?"
"John," said the Voice,
"you have been dedicate to me from birth,
confirmed by your own decision and devotion.
I now have need of you,
and summon you
to be my Messenger.
The people wait in anxious expectation.
My Kingdom is about to come in power.
Preach ye:
   Proclaim the Good News.
Here in the wilderness—
   as Isaiah foretold—

you shall make ready my Road,
prepare the Way of the Lord."

I obeyed,
and preached with fierce joy:
"Repent ye,
for the Kingdom of God is at hand.
God is visiting his people in anger.
Repent, be baptized,
and receive forgiveness for your sins."
At first I spoke to caravans
stopped in the desert for the night.
The word went forth.
Soon many from the cities
came in crowds to hear.

I said to them:
"You brood of vipers,
children of the serpent,
offspring of the devil,
who warned you to flee
from the wrath to come?
Bear fruit that befits repentance.
Do not trust in descent from Abraham.
God will keep the Covenant
with Abraham's seed,
but it need not be you.
God will raise up new seed to Abraham,

56

if necessary, from these desert stones,
and the promise of the Covenant
will be fulfilled to them.
Even now the axe is laid
to the foot of the trees;
every tree that does not bear good fruit
will be cut down and burned.
Those who have much,
    share with the poor.
Creditors,
    collect no more than is due.
Policemen,
    rob none, make no false arrests,
    and take no graft."

Soon they began to ask if I were Christ.
"No," I replied,
"I am the Forerunner,
the Messenger.
After me there comes one
who is far mightier than I,
whose sandals I am not worthy to unloose,
and whose feet I am not worthy to wash.
I baptize you with water,
but he will baptize you
with the Holy Spirit
and with fire.
His winnowing fork is in his hand.

He will clear the threshing floor
and gather the wheat in his granary.
The chaff he will burn
with unquenchable fire—
not in some Hell,
distant in time and space,
but here and soon."

I preached against Herod,
his collaboration with the Romans,
his disregard for our Law and customs,
his introduction of the Gentile ways,
and for sleeping with the divorced wife
of his brother Philip.
That is why I am here
within the cold walls of Machaerus Castle
on the eastern shore of the Dead Sea.

Herodias will never let me go.
Herod, half in hate and half in fear,
is all uncertain what he ought to do.
If left alone, he would perhaps free me.
He is enough a Jew to recognize
I am God's Prophet.
But the Whore of Herod will prevail.
Somehow—and soon—
she will destroy my life.

*T*housands came to hear—and believed.
Thousands were baptized in the Jordan.
And yet more thousands came in swelling flood.
Among them was Andrew of Bethsaida,
who became my disciple.
One day he brought Jesus.
As I preached, I caught his eye;
he seemed deeply stirred.
Thereafter he came several times.

Another day, when I called the repentants
to be baptized,
Jesus entered the water.
I knew that he was good,
had done no man harm,
and asked why he sought baptism of me.

With the disturbing smile
which had always enraged me,
he told me I owed him a cleansing
for the stains—
   inside and out—
which my rough teasing had caused him,
and asked if I had a prejudice
against baptizing relatives.
When I prayed for the converts,
a shaft of sunlight
thrust downward from the overcast sky

and bathed him in radiance.
His warm skin gleamed,
and his beard seemed on fire.
His eyes glowed with a more than earthly light.
I felt a power at work
and the spirit of God seemed to settle in him.

*F*or a time he continued with me.
Then I heard he was preaching in the cities.
At first he sounded my call to repentance,
but later I heard disturbing reports.
His nature was never austere like mine.
He was preaching not of God's anger,
but of God's love and forgiveness.
People were crowding to hear him.
He spoke of the Kingdom of God
as already in existence,
the community of the forgiven,
bearing wrong with patience,
neutralizing evil with love,
and doing good until it hurts.
With forgiveness
he brought healing,
and many mighty works
were told of him.
Some of my disciples turned to him.
I heard rumors

that God had visited his people,
that Jesus had been hailed as the Messiah.

Here from my prison cell
I sent word to him,
"Are you he who is to come,
or shall we look for another?"
And Jesus answered my disciples,
"Go and tell John
what you have seen and heard.
The blind receive their sight,
the deaf hear,
the lame walk,
the dumb speak,
lepers are cleansed,
the dead are raised up,
and the poor have good news preached to them.
Blessed is he
who takes no offense at me."

I know the writings of Isaiah;
surely he refers to them.
Listen:

> In that day the deaf shall hear
>   the words of a book,
> and out of their gloom and darkness
>   the eyes of the blind shall see.

The meek shall obtain fresh joy in the
Lord,
and the poor among men shall exult
in the Holy One of Israel.*

And again:

Say to those who are of a fearful heart
"Be strong, fear not!
Behold, your God
will come with vengeance;
with the recompense of God
He will come and save you."

Then the eyes of the blind shall be
opened,
and the ears of the deaf unstopped;
then shall the lame man leap like a hart,
and the tongue of the dumb sing for
joy.

For waters shall break forth in the
wilderness,
and streams in the desert;
the burning sand shall become a pool,
and the thirsty ground springs of
water . . .

And a highway shall be there,
and it shall be called the Holy Way;

* Isaiah 29:18-19.

the unclean shall not pass over it,
and fools shall not err therein.
No lion shall be there,
nor shall any ravenous beast come
upon it;
they shall not be found there,
but the redeemed shall walk there.

And the ransomed of the Lord shall
return,
and come to Zion with singing,
with everlasting joy upon their heads;
they shall obtain joy and gladness,
and sorrow and sighing shall flee
away.*

He can refer to nothing else than these.
And these can mean but one thing:
the things that were prophesied
for the time of the Messiah have occurred.
The Messiah must be here.
Jesus is he.
Jesus is Lord.
He answers in this way
because to proclaim himself as Messiah
would mean his death.
I am the waters
which broke forth in the desert.

* Isaiah 35:4-10.

I made the straight road
which he shall call *The Way*.
Yes.
This is what he means.
But is it so?
Is he the Messiah?
Or is he deluded?

*M*y work is done.
I sit here alone
waiting for a death
that seems sure.
I am not afraid to die.
My disciples are faithful,
but they can do nothing for me.
I would like to know
that my work was useful
and successful.
I would like to see the Messiah,
whose coming I have foretold,
enthroned in glory.
I would like to be sure
that the voice I obeyed
was of God, and not illusion.

Can Jesus ben Joseph be the Christ?
I cannot send my disciples to him;
I am eaten by uncertainty.
Can he really be the Christ?

I know him too well to believe.
He is not the Messiah I looked for.
He is too gentle.
There is not the force in him
that is needed
to push salvation to completion.
And I cannot accept a frivolous Messiah
feasting with the rich
in terms of fellowship.

Yet he speaks as the Suffering Servant
in the voice of Isaiah.
I am torn by doubt.
O God, give thy faithful servant
the assurance of work well done.

> Hear my cry, O God,
> listen to my prayer;
> from the end of the earth I call to thee,
> when my heart is faint.

> Lead thou me
> to the rock that is higher than I;
> for thou art my refuge,
> a strong tower against the enemy.

> Let me dwell in thy tent for ever!
> Oh to be safe under the shelter of thy
> wings!

For thou, O God, hast heard my vows,
Thou hast given me the heritage of those
who fear thy name.

Prolong the life of the king;
may his years endure to all generations!
May he be enthroned for ever before
God;
bid steadfast love and faithfulness
watch over him!

So will I ever sing praises to thy name,
as I pay my vows day after day.*

* Psalm 61.

III

The Mother at Capernaum

Mary's account of a painful rebuff at the hands of her son, Rabbi Jesus. "Family" is defined.

Note on the Personality of Mary

The following section is reverently meant. It catches Mary the Mother at a moment when she is deeply distressed over something she cannot understand. Jesus uses the occasion of her visit to define the family of God. But she could not have comprehended this at the time.

The Gospels seem clear that during her son's life Mary did not understand or approve his ministry. Later, after the Passion and Resurrection and John's instruction in their meaning, she gained spiritual maturity through her suffering and has become the symbol of understanding sympathy for the world's pain.

Here Mary is not the grand lady of the manor as she was envisioned during the Middle Ages. She is shown as a simple countrywoman, puzzled, bewildered, and hurt, trying desperately to meet a major crisis without the support and guidance of a husband. She voices the usual reactions of conventional wisdom when brought face to face with the unconventional mystery that is Jesus Christ.

The Mother at Capernaum

*H*e would not see me.
He would not see me—
me, his mother!
He would not let me in.

We—his mother and his brothers—
stood waiting at the door
of the house where he was,
and he would not let us in.
He would not stop his endless talking
  with his friends
to speak to us.

He has lost his mind.
I have to face it at last:
my son has lost his mind.
He is beside himself!

*S*uch a good boy he was,
bright-eyed and watchful from his cradle,
from when I first called him my little Messiah.
So quick to learn—so smart.

69

The pride of Rabbi Solomon:
he called him his best pupil ever.

Once, in the Temple,
he talked with the Elders
and amazed them all—
such big words he used.
Would you believe it—
he was only twelve.

Always kind and thoughtful he was,
never too busy at games
   to answer his mother.
How he loved his father Joseph,
followed him everywhere,
watched him do his work,
and tried every tool.
From a baby, he would toss the sawdust
   to see it float
and play with the shavings.
A good carpenter he became—
   like his father—
none better.
Good chests he made,
with drawers that fit,
and strong furniture.
But best of all were the yokes he made for oxen—
   Joseph taught him.
Nobody in all Galilee could make

    such a good fit,
each one just right
for the beast which was to wear it.
Always the shoulders fit easy into it,
and it made light the burden to be dragged.
None of my other boys—and they are good—
can do yokes half so well.

Joseph was so proud—
I am glad he's dead!
I am glad he did not live to see this day.
Me—his wife—shamed,
and by his firstborn son
who was his pride and joy—
who now is mad.

*A*n unhappy day it was
when he went off to hear
his cousin preach.
His cousin John,
that no-good who ran off into the desert
and got his head cut off
for criticizing his betters.
A real wildman, that one—
wearing skins and eating insects.
What a big mouth he had.
"Repent ye!"
If his old father had been alive,

he would have helped him repent
at the business end of a strap.

But my son was a good boy.
Quiet sometimes, and thoughtful—
nobody thought he'd get religion.
But he did, and the worst way.
Was he satisfied to be a priest
   and serve in the Temple,
or a Rabbi, and minister to a nice
   well-behaved congregation?
Not him!
He has to be a missionary
to the no-good poor, scum of the earth,
and tell them—what pigs wouldn't eat with—
that God is their Father and loves them,
that all men are their brothers.
Imagine!

Always with the good people of the town
he was. He liked the old ones;
much time he spent with them.
Now he runs about the world
with wild fishermen, tax collectors,
outcasts, wild-lifes, and radicals.
He insults the learned Pharisees
and other men of dignity and substance,
calling them liars and hypocrites,
blasphemers of the Holy Spirit,

and stinking tombstones.
My boy is mad.

Never he looked at a woman,
except his mother,
until he was thirty
    and got religion.
Now, everywhere he goes—
    open and defiant—
is seen that wanton hussy,
Mary of Magdala,
making sheep's eyes at him.
And all the world knows
    what she is.
How could he do it, even if he's crazy?
And him so well brought up.

So many miles we came—
my other sons and me—
to take him home,
to treat him gentle,
to keep him safe
    and quiet.
But he won't see us.
He won't see me—his own mother.
Would you believe it!
And him a man of God!
He denies us.

73

He says that we are not related.
   "Those who do the will of my Father in
      Heaven,
   They are my mother, and sister, and brother."
Was a mother ever so humiliated?
We came seeking, asking, and knocking—
   like he says—
and the door was slammed in our faces!

That "Father" he talks about,
whose will he is doing—
he never learned that from Joseph.
   Dear, gentle Joseph.
I'm sure that I try to be a good woman,
   a good mother.
I am not schooled,
but I try to keep on the right side of God
and raise my family to do right.
My son has gone crazy
and blames it on God.
He calls him "Father,"
which sounds flippant and familiar
and somehow undignified, I'm sure.
Does he think even God loves him
   like I do?

*H*e had better be careful.
If he calls God "Father,"

someone may call him "God's Son" or "Messiah"
and then he will be in trouble.
Any poor boy who goes into politics
can expect to end on a cross.
And where will his "Father" be then?
Does he think *he* would save him?

Well, we must go home.
He won't come with us.
He won't even see us.
And there are too many of his "friends"
to take him by force.
I bet they laugh at him behind his back!
I am afraid.
I wish I could see him this once,
just for a minute.
He is my son, and I love him.
I am afraid that the next time I see him
he will be dead—or dying.

A mother's life is hard.
She bears her boy with pain,
works to feed and clothe him,
with pride watches him grow,
glories in his strength and brains,
then loses him to some woman—
    or to God—
watches him throw himself away

and with him her hopes, dreams, and joy.
Who knows how he will turn out?

I have lost this, my son.
I am insulted, hurt, and sore afraid.
But I hope that I will be spared one thing:
I hope my boy won't become a common criminal
and end up on a cross.
I couldn't stand that.
A father might stand by,
but no mother could.

IV

Sound Investment

Matthew, disciple and ex-tax collector, tells how he entertained Rabbi Jesus and accepted a return invitation which led to a new job involving more work at less pay.

Sound Investment

I am Matthew,
disciple and friend
of our Lord Jesus the Messiah
and supporter of his church.
I was once a publican,
a collector of Roman taxes,
and rich in worldly goods.
I have given all to the cause
and am now a poor man
in the eyes of the world.
In my own eyes,
I am infinitely richer
in those things that matter most.
In trying to do good,
as Jesus himself taught me,
I have been richly rewarded
in the acquisition of self-respect
and the companionship of friends.

In a very real sense,
it's just a matter of sound business.
In my search for money,
I was very successful—

not immensely wealthy
by Roman patrician standards,
but very well-fixed.
My children will never have to work—
    as I did—
to earn their daily bread.
But I was not satisfied.
Something essential was lacking.
Then I met the Master;
he raised my standards
and revised my goals.
My family was provided for
by a solid endowment,
and I used the rest for his purposes.
I have never regretted it.

*I*t all began with a party.
As even you Gentiles may know,
we publicans are not popular.
The price of our profits
is disloyalty to our traditions
and collaboration with the enemy.
We are looked upon as traitors
to our nation and our God.
A leper, although set apart,
may worship in a synagogue.
No taxgatherer is permitted to worship.
No good Jew, however poor,

will accept alms from us.
We are social and moral outcasts.

My own case was even worse.
I am of the House of Levi;
my career labeled me an unfrocked priest.
Of course,
our little country
could not stand alone
in the modern world—
there is no place
for ethnic self-determination
in a world state—
and some must realize this
and cooperate with Rome.
But I have no heart
to defend the publicans.
Their chief accusers
come from within.
They know they do wrong
and earn the contempt of their fellows,
so they despise themselves.

I was not a big collector
like Zacchaeus of Jericho,
but had the customhouse at Capernaum.
It was my duty to inspect, examine, and assess
all goods that were shipped in or
   through the city.

Capernaum is an important post
not only for its shipping; the caravan road
from Damascus to the Mediterranean Sea
runs through it, and it lies near the border
of Galilee and the neighboring Tetrarchy of
      Philip.
My office was a booth down near the harbor.
The Master often came and spoke to crowds
which gathered in the square on which it
      fronted.
I heard him once or twice, but was too busy
pursuing gain to pay him any heed.

*O*ne day I heard him waxing eloquent
about the coming Kingdom of the Lord
for which all were invited to prepare.
It made me angry. If such kingdom came,
no welcome would be there for such as I.
I shouted from my door,
"You talk big, Rabbi,
inviting sinners who repent to join
and find salvation in your kingdom-come.
Show the crowd here how far you would go
in seeking out and saving all who sin.
I here invite you come and dine with me.
We'll have a party. Be my honored guest.
You may bring all your friends; I'll summon
      mine.

82

I'll serve the very best my house provides
and even give you chance to preach to us."

Rabbi Jesus smiled,
   "Who are you, my friend?"
I watched his face
to see it turn to fear.
"Levi, the Publican,"
I replied.
His smile deepened,
   "Your name and work conflict;
   I like it not.
   Since you do offer feast
   and chance to preach,
   henceforth I'll call you 'Matthew,'
   'Gift of God.'
   So may you ever prove.
   As for your invitation,
   I accept. Just name the time,
   I'll gladly dine with you
   and with your friends.
   When we are better acquainted,
   I may return an invitation."

The crowd murmured in mingled horror and
   protest.
I quickly said, "I need but little time,
good Rabbi; come to me tomorrow night."
He said,

"Call me not 'good,'
for God alone is good.
I come not to be good
but to lead you to goodness.
Consider it a date."
I bowed my gratitude.

As I was leaving,
I heard a Pharisee within the crowd
berating him for all his careless ways,
call him unclean, lawbreaker, glutton, drunk,
Sabbath-violator, corrupter of the young,
and other terms of serious reproach.
The Rabbi answered. I heard not his words,
but caught the pointed banter of his tone.
The crowd was laughing as I went away.

*T*he morrow both seemed long
    and went too fast.
I burned with hope to see him;
yet feared he would not come.
Every tax collector
and successful sinner
for miles around
accepted my invitation.
Everything was made ready.
As is the custom,
I sent word to the Rabbi's house

that all was in readiness
and that he was expected.
My friends arrived early.
As my hopes were fading,
the Rabbi appeared.
Three friends were with him.
I met them at the door
and greeted them joyfully,
"Hail and welcome to this poor house,
worthy Rabbi and friends."
As host, I kissed him on the cheek,
and bent my head
to receive his answering kiss
on the forehead as a blessing.

I exchanged kisses also
with his disciples,
and turned them over to the servants
for the ministrations of welcome.
Then I addressed Rabbi Jesus,
"Rabbi, your visit
honors this house
as never before.
Let me minister to you
as your servant."
So saying,
I removed his cloak and coat,
seated him on a bench,
brought warmed water,

washed his face, hands, and feet,
and dried them with a napkin.
I clothed him in a seamless tunic
of flawless workmanship,
white in color and of the softest linen,
more costly than the woolen one he wore,
saying,
"Rabbi,
accept this coat—
together with this sleeved mantle of brown linen
and a girdle of golden color,
which my servants will place on you
before you go—
as an expression of my gratitude
for your coming.
May they continue to serve you
as I seek to do this day."
He answered me,
    "Sir, you receive me in love,
    and I accept in kind.
    Your gift will be treasured—
        and remembered."

Then, placing the napkin around his neck
to protect the coat,
I anointed his hair and beard
with oil spiced with nard,
and—he being the honored guest—

placed on his head
a laurel wreath entwined with flowers.
I led him thus attired unto the feast.
He seemed much moved by his reception.

The banquet hall was gay and festive,
arranged in the Roman manner.
Three square tables formed a "U"
open toward the door.
The surfaces had been scrubbed
and were spotless.
Around them were couches
sufficient to accommodate the guests,
most of whom were in their places.
Several reclined on each couch
at an angle to the table,
each supported by his left arm
with his right hand free for eating.
Thus placed, each overlapped his neighbor
and seemed to lean on the bosom
of the one who lay behind him.
Since this was a formal feast,
no women were invited.
I presented the guest of honor
to the company.
All rose to greet him,
and I presented each to him in turn.

As I led him to the place of honor
at the far side of the center table,
I was embarrassed to ask him—
    in this place—
to utter grace.
He saw through my confusion
and put me at my ease:
    "Your courtesy does me honor.
    Before we take our places
    let us ask God's blessing
    on this feast. Great God,
    who seeth deep in all men's hearts,
    bestow thy blessing on all gathered here.
    Bless thou this food unto our nourishment,
    fill thou our nurtured bodies with thy grace,
    and fix our quickened minds upon thy will."

It was nicely done.
I felt the guests relax.
I issued orders
that the food be served,
and settled back
to take full joy of it.

All formal Jewish feasts
are of two parts,
referred to generally
as "the Bread" and "the Wine."

We do not serve
wine with the food.
For the first portion of the evening,
the guests are relatively quiet;
there is little conversation
and the major attention is directed
to the various dishes being served.
Then, at the appropriate time,
when appetites are sated
and the spicy food has made all thirsty,
the host or steward of the feast
orders the uneaten food removed
and the wine to be brought and blessed.
Then the guests rouse themselves
to some serious drinking,
lively conversation,
and (often rowdy) entertainment.

It is the custom
to appoint one of the guests
as governor of the feast.
It is his responsibility
to supervise the servants,
see that all are satisfied,
and later function
as master of ceremonies.
Since I did not dare
thrust this duty upon the Rabbi,
and none other was worthy,

I served as my own steward.
As the food was served,
I signaled the hired quartet
of female musicians to begin.
During the first part of the evening
they played almost constantly,
masking the noises of eating
with the sweet, soft sounds
of flute, pipes, and harp.
Occasionally, one of the players
would blend her voice with the instruments
in the florid, wordless glossolalia
so popular with us of late.

*S*ix slaves served the various viands.
First a stack of wheat loaves—
    parchment thin—
was set on the table at each place.
Then bowls of lamb and lentil stew,
generously flavored with onions,
were placed on the table.
Fingers were thrust into the shallow bowls
to pursue the pieces of meat,
and were cleansed by licking
or by wiping on the bread
which in turn was used
to scoop up the lentils

90

or sop up the gravy.
Most of us used nothing else,
but there was a silver plate
for the guest of honor,
on which I placed generous portions
of the best pieces,
those heavy with fat.

After came the roast fowl
seasoned with spices
and a nut dressing.
These were well cooked,
and desired portions
were pulled off with the fingers.
Then were offered veal and peppers,
roasted and served on a spit.
Pieces were taken with the bread
which was rolled around them,
making tasty portions.

When the guests began to lose interest
and to refuse offered dishes,
various fruits and cakes were brought.
There were pomegranates, dates, citron,
and choice first-fruit figs.
Some of the cakes were baked in ovens,
then coated with honey
and sprinkled with spices or nuts.

Others were deep-fried in olive oil
and melted in the mouth.

*W*hile all dishes were prepared
according to Jewish Law,
the Master asked no questions
and accepted everything.
Although he lived the spirit of the Law,
I saw he heeded custom
only so far as it was sensible
and to avoid needless offense.
I asked him, "Rabbi,
what made you accept my invitation?"
He answered,
   "To do God's will
   and to get a good meal.
   I congratulate you on your cook.
   It is a pity a prophet
   must eat with backsliders
   to be well fed."

There was general laughter,
and we began to ply him with questions.
"Rabbi, when you agreed
to come tonight,
the Pharisees were outraged.
We are not respectable.

What answer can you make
to their criticisms?"

Jesus answered,
   "Then Matthew—
   for so I renamed our host yesterday—
   did not tell you my answer to them?
   I said to the learned Pharisees:
   You Pharisees keep the Law,
   are therefore without sin,
   and to offer you salvation
   would be a presumption—
     for either God or me.
   I am a doctor to the spirit.
   Those who are well
   have no need of a physician,
   but only those who are sick.
   I came, not to call the righteous,
   but to call sinners to repentance.
   And how can you save a man
   if you won't eat with him?"

One asked,
"Rabbi, do you expect
to do a big business here?"

He replied,
   "If in this company

93

a sheep can be referred to
without having it fleeced,
I should like to tell you wolves
about a little, lost sheep.
A certain shepherd
has a hundred sheep.
One day, he notices
that one is missing,
and he knows it has wandered off
and gotten lost.
What does the shepherd do?
Of course.
He leaves the ninety-nine
on the hill where they are safe,
and goes to seek
the one that is lost.
And if he finds it,
truly, I say to you,
he rejoices over it
more than over the others
that never went astray.

"It is not the will
of my Father who is in Heaven
that a single one
of you dear little sheep
in wolves' clothing
should perish."

(Hearty chuckles were heard about the room.)
  "My Father and I
  invite each and all of you
  to join with us.
  While it would be nice,
  I don't really expect
  a mass conversion
  here tonight.
  But I am willing
  to go all out
  in a search for just one.
  If tonight results
  in the salvation of one soul,
  the Father and I
  will be filled with rejoicing.
  And even if not one of you is saved,
  I shall enjoy my visit here this night."

I saw that the eating was ended,
signaled for the food to be removed,
and ordered that the wine be brought.
Taking a flagon of good Syrian wine—
the choice wine of Helbon—
I handed it to the Master and said,
"Rabbi, you blessed the Bread
to such good purpose!
Will you bless also the Wine?"

95

Jesus took the flagon
and filled a gold cup
which had been placed before him.
Holding the cup aloft, he spoke:
   "To you, our generous host,
   many thanks for your hospitality.
   Country preachers are chronically hungry,
   but you have labored hard
   to cure me of it. I feel
   that I should never hunger again.
   But now, to him who is the ultimate host
   of every banquet let us again
   offer thanks for the good things he has given,
   and ask his blessing
   on the goodness and gaiety which is to come."

And saying this,
he saluted the company with his cup
and sipped the wine.

Rabbi," asked old Mordecai,
his fat sides heaving
and his button-eyes frankly curious,
"the disciples of John fast often
and have set periods for prayer.
And so do the Pharisees
and their disciples.

96

But here are you and your disciples,
eating heartily and drinking wine.
Aren't you afraid
of setting us sinners
a bad example?"

The Master replied,
　"John's disciples and the Pharisees
　are indeed men of rectitude.
　And their faces are as melancholy
　as their pious propriety.
　God wishes us to be good
　and to be glad at the same time.
　The Pharisees must learn
　what God means when—
　through his prophets—
　he says: 'I desire mercy,
　and not sacrifice.'
　God desires personal righteousness,
　not ritual sanctity;
　and requires only that you
　live justly, show mercy,
　and walk humbly in his presence
　as a dutiful son.

　"I am not a Nazirite—
　punishing myself to be good.
　Tonight I am a happy
　glutton and winebibber—

97

as they accuse me—
relaxing and strengthening myself
for redoubled efforts tomorrow
in my work for the Kingdom.
After all, my time on this earth
with my disciples will be short.
Can the wedding guests mourn
as long as the bridegroom is with them?
The days will come
when the bridegroom is taken away,
and then will be time enough
for fasting.
But I am not yet ready
to preach to you.
The musicians are prepared to sing.
Pass the wine around again,
and then, when our cups are full,
let us listen to their song.
I heed the sage advice
of the grandson of Sirach, who says:

    'Temper your wisdom,
    so not to disturb the singing.
    When wine is present,
    do not pour out discourse,
    and flaunt not your wisdom
    at the wrong time.' *

* Ecclesiasticus (Sirach) 32:3-4. Confraternity Version, by permission.

I promise to be silent.
What are they going to give us?"

I answered him,
"Sir, they sing a drinking song
dear to the hearts of publicans,
taken from the words of the wicked
in the Book of Wisdom.
It expresses our philosophy.
Sing, musicians!"

The harpist then,
in a full rich contralto,
sang the following song
to her own accompaniment:
"Come, let us enjoy the good things that are
real,
and use the freshness of creation eagerly.
Let us have our fill of costly wine and
perfumes,
and let no springtime blossoms pass us by.

"Let us crown ourselves with rosebuds ere
they wither;
let no meadow be free from our wantonness.
Everywhere let us leave tokens of our rejoicing,
for this our portion is, and this our lot.

"Let us squeeze the just man in his hour of
need

and spare neither the widow nor the aged.
Let strength be our standard of justice and
   right,
with contempt for those whose weakness
   proves them worthless." *

*T*he Rabbi seemed saddened
by our song, and spoke to us:
   "The melody is lovely,
   but the words are sick.
   If that is your philosophy,
   you need a new song,
   and you need me
   to doctor your sickness.

   "I am glad I came.
   The world was not made
   solely for your entertainment.
   He who preaches pleasure
   as the end of man
   is a false prophet.
   God has a purpose
   for each life
   within his Kingdom,
   and man's best joy
   is to find his place
   doing God's will.

* Wisdom of Solomon 2:6-11. (Paraphrase.)

"Do not lay up for yourselves
treasures on earth,
where moth and rust consume
and thieves break in and steal;
but lay up for yourselves
treasures in heaven,
where there is neither moth nor rust
and thieves may not enter.
For where you put your treasure,
there will your heart be also.

"No man can serve two masters,
for either he will hate the one
and love the other,
or he will be devoted to the one
and despise the other.
You cannot serve
both God and mammon.

"It is the ancient custom
at our feasts
to ask and answer riddles.
Listen, and I will put to you a puzzle:
How is the soul of man
like a fig tree?
What say you?"

We pondered long
and puzzled loud

over his riddle.
Many involved
and ingenious answers
were suggested.
Some said that both
are the product of the soil
in which they have grown
and of the roots
which sustain them;
others that their health
  may be judged
by the condition of their skin.
But no solution satisfied.

Then the Rabbi gave his answer.
  "Both the soul of man
  and the virtue of the fig tree
  are judged by their fruits.
  Are grapes gathered from thorns,
  or figs from thistles?
  Every sound tree bears good fruit,
  but the bad tree bears evil fruit.
  A sound tree cannot bear evil fruit,
  nor can a bad tree bear good fruit.
  Every tree that does not bear good fruit
  is cut down and cast into the fire.
  So can you tell false prophets and false men;
  you will know them by their fruits."

102

The company applauded
with enthusiasm,
and many looked thoughtful.

*F*or a while the conversation
became more general.
Everyone had a good time.
The wine passed often,
and the Master joined
in every toast,
but his easy friendliness
was not impaired.

After a time,
I watered the wine
in the Roman manner,
and at no time in the evening
did I serve the spiced wine
which foams and inflames.
But even so,
some of the more boisterous
of my friends
had to be cautioned and restrained
out of deference to our guest.

*A*ll evening his conversation
was spicy and brilliant.

He proposed riddles,
related parables,
and told simple stories
with humor and drama.
His imagery was unrestrained,
and his love of paradox
was evident.
He told one wealthy man
that it was easier for a camel
to crawl through the eye of a needle
than for a rich man
to enter the Kingdom of Heaven.

"Then we here all are lost,"
complained my friend.
   "Not so," he replied.
   "The gate is narrow
and the way is hard,
but you can get in.
It will be easier for you
than for the Pharisees,
for you know you sin,
but they are armored
with false righteousness
against salvation.
If with all your hearts
you ask, and seek, and knock,
you will be admitted.
What man of you,

if his son asks him for bread,
will give him a stone?
Or if he asks for a fish,
will give him a snake?
If you then,
who are evil,
know how to give good gifts
to your children,
how much more
will your Father in Heaven
give good things
to those who ask him?"

Then he acted out
a little play,
and made the characters
come vividly to life.
Every tone and gesture
were perfect.
He told how two men
went up into the temple to pray.
One was a Pharisee
and the other a tax collector.
The Pharisee stood
and prayed thus to himself:
    "God, I thank thee
    that I am not like other men,
        extortioners,
            unjust,

105

adulterers,
or even like this miserable tax collector.
I fast twice every week.
I give you one tenth
of all that I get.
Help me remain
as pleasing to you
as I have been."

His nose was in the air;
every expression, every gesture,
revealed the colossal self-satisfaction
of the Pharisee.
Then he told of the tax collector,
standing afar off,
who would not even
lift up his eyes to heaven,
but humbly knelt
and beat his breast in shame,
saying:
   "God,
   be merciful to me,
   a sinner."

Then Jesus said,
   "I tell you this man
   went back to his house forgiven,
   rather than the other.

He who humbles himself in repentance
will be exalted in God's mercy."

*T*here was much more
that I cannot now remember.
There was much singing,
both of love songs and of hymns,
and by both the musicians
and the guests.
The Rabbi had a lovely voice
and sang several folk songs
of our people.
Two of the musicians danced solos,
and the Rabbi led the guests
in a sacred dance
to the accompaniment of a psalm
sung by us all.
It was a joyous evening
that I shall never forget,
nor—I believe—
will any who were present.

After my guests had left—
the Master strikingly handsome
in his new robe—
I sought my bed,
but could not sleep.
The events of the evening

and the new ideas
presented by the teacher
whirled in my head.
I was strongly stirred by what he said,
but more by what he revealed.
I saw God's love for me
shining out of his eyes.
I could not draw back from that look,
or reject that love.

*T*he dawn of a new day
finally arrived.
I was early at my booth
down by the harbor.
But I was disturbed and unhappy;
nothing seemed right.
I was impatient with the haggling
over the duties to be assessed,
and lost my temper three times.
My life seemed more
than I could bear.

Then the Master came by.
He was clad in his new clothes
and seemed radiant.
He looked at me
as I sat at the tax window,
and smiled as he said,

108

"Matthew, I told you
that after we were better acquainted
I might issue you an invitation.
I feel we are now old friends.
Come, Matthew, follow me."

I was suddenly and inexpressibly glad.
A feeling of warmth and joy
poured over me.
I knew that I wished to be with him
doing God's work
for the rest of my life.
Without a single word
I rose,
    closed my booth,
        and followed him.
I have walked with him
ever since.

In late years,
I have been the teacher of the young
both here and in Damascus.
For some time now,
I have been toying with the idea
of writing an account
of our Lord's teaching and ministry.
Already, I have a collection
of his most celebrated sayings.

The Master's work
is bigger than our country.
Paul and others
have carried his Gospel
over the length and breadth of the Empire.
His Word has gone out to the nations.

He is more than the Jewish Messiah;
he is the Savior of the whole world.
Someday the world will know it
and will be interested in what he said,
   how he lived,
     and what he was like.
Since the destruction of Jerusalem,
there are few of us still living
who actually knew and remember him.
He did not come soon again as we had thought,
and I believe we need a longer view
to carry us through troubled times ahead.

A new generation has arisen,
and there is need of a written Gospel,
setting forth the new order
and the New Covenant,
to instruct and inform them.
Since Judas is dead,
I am the only one of the original fellowship
with the education and training to do it.
I have always had a good sense of organization,

have a full knowledge of Jewish customs,
and could demonstrate how Jesus fulfills
the best messianic traditions.
Who knows, I may yet put to use
the sound legal education
which is the only asset I have salvaged
from an otherwise misspent youth.
You see, I am doing a self-selling job
and will yet talk myself into it.

If I do write it,
I know one thing it will contain.
Thucydides—in his history of the Peloponnesian
 War—
makes Pericles really come alive
in the reports of his speeches.
I believe somewhat the same thing
can and should be done for Jesus.
If I write that book,
it will contain at least one
full-length and blazing sermon of our Lord
that will reveal the power, thrust, and depth
of his fine mind, in all its tempered strength,
complete with love of pun and paradox.
It will be a sermon to remember.

V

The Bad Samaritan

A sinful Samaritan woman tells of an intimate conversation over a cup of water with Jesus of Nazareth.

The Bad Samaritan

*T*he Master passed this way.
I saw him and he spoke to me.
Things will not be the same again.

I am a Samaritan,
a woman of the village of Sychar,
which is near the field that Jacob
gave to his son Joseph.
Jacob's well is here,
some distance from the town.
The water lies far below the surface
and is reached only with effort.
Twice daily do we women of the town
take our clay water jars upon our heads
and go to fill and bring them home again.
There is much gossip and exchange of news,
in which I had but little part
for most were not cordial.
I must admit
my reputation was not good.
So usually I went at midday
and avoided the others.

*W*e Samaritans
are a sort of cousin to the Jews.
When Assyria smashed the Northern Kingdom
and the ten Hebrew tribes were taken away,
foreign settlers were imported
who mingled with the native Hebrew stock
to repeople the country.
Our religion is much the same as the Jews'.
We revere Moses
and accept only his books—
the Pentateuch—as scripture.
We seek to observe the Law
as we understand it.
But our temple
is at Mount Gerizim,
not Jerusalem,
and we have our own High Priests,
rituals, and festivals.
Along with the Jews,
we look for the coming Messiah
who will usher in
a new Golden Age.

*O*ne day,
as I came early to the well,
I saw seated at its top
a most interesting-looking man.
He was alone;

116

I learned later that his companions
had gone on to the village
to procure food.
Although he was hot and tired
and his face lined with fatigue or thought,
he was extremely handsome
in an almost Grecian way,
but sufficiently strong of feature
to escape being called beautiful.
His hair and beard were warmly russet
in the evening sun.
His cloak—though dusty—
was of good quality,
and its style proclaimed him a Jew.

I knew he was thirsty
and wanted a drink,
and I knew too he hoped
that I would offer it unasked.
These high and mighty Jews
have no dealings with Samaritans
and will not talk to any women in public,
not even their own wives.

But I had made many men—
often against their wills—
do more than talk to me.
I saw to it,
as I made a production

117

of drawing the water,
that he could not but be aware
of my considerable attractions.
I was determined
to make him speak to me,
for I had learned
that in many respects
all men are alike—
and we were alone.

*A*nd he did speak.
He said to me,
   "Will you give me a drink?"
I looked shyly at him.
His eyes were laughing at me.
So I played demure
and hesitated,
then gave him to drink.
He drank long, and thanked me.

I did not hurry off.
I am not afraid of men.
He was good to look at
and had been pleasant,
and there were few
for me to talk with.
So I said to him,
"How is it that you,

118

a Jew,
ask a drink of me,
a woman of Samaria?"
And he answered me,
  "I speak to women as well as men.
  If you knew the gift of God,
  and who it is who says to you
  'Give me a drink,'
  you would have asked of me,
  and I would have given you,
  living water."

I was not sure what he meant;
men had offered before this
to pour themselves out for me.
He seemed to offer love,
but a different love
than I had ever known,
no less compelling,
and more satisfying
to my sated spirit.
But I had been fooled before,
so temporized
and answered him,
"Sir, you have nothing to draw with,
and the well is deep;
where do you get
that living water?

119

Are you greater
than our Father Jacob,
who gave us the well,
and drank from it himself,
and his sons, and his cattle?"

He said to me,
    "Every one who drinks of this water
    will thirst again,
    but whoever drinks of the water
    that I shall give him
    will never thirst.
    The water that I shall give him
    will become in him a spring of water
    welling up to eternal life."
And I said to him,
"Sir, give me this water,
that I may not thirst,
nor come here to draw."

*A*nd he said,
    "Go,
    call your husband,
    and return here."
I was startled.
He was not flirting.
I would have gone anywhere with him,
but he was serious,

with a meaning too deep
for me to know.
So I said to him,
"I have no husband."

He replied to me,
  "You are right in saying
  'I have no husband';
  for you have had
  several husbands,
  and the man you now have
  is not your husband.
  So you speak truly."

I was confused.
He read my life
like an open scroll,
and as seen with his eyes
it looked ugly.
So I sought
to change the subject,
"Sir, I perceive
that you are a prophet.
Our fathers worshiped
on this mountain,
and you say in Jerusalem
is the place where men
ought to worship."

He said to me,
  "Woman, believe me,
  the hour is coming
  when neither on this mountain
  nor in Jerusalem
  will the Father be worshiped.
  You worship what you do not know;
  we worship what we know,
  for salvation is from the Jews.
  But the hour is coming,
  and now is,
  when the true worshipers
  will worship the Father
  in spirit and truth,
  for such the Father seeks
  to worship him.
  God is spirit,
  and those who worship him
  must worship in spirit and truth."

*T*his was pretty deep
for a sinful woman,
but I said to him,
"I know that Messiah,
who is called Christ,
is coming.
When he comes,
he will show us all things."

122

He answered,
   "I who speak to you
   am he."

*J*ust then his companions came.
They were astonished
to see him talking with a woman,
but said nothing.
I left my water jar
and hurried to the village,
and said to the people,
"Come, see a man
who told me all
that I ever did.
Can this be the Christ?"
They went out of the village
and hastened to him.

Many of the villagers
believed in him
because of my testimony.
So when they came to him,
they asked him to stay with them.
He stayed here two days,
and many more believed
because of his words.
They said to me,
"It is no longer

123

because of your words
that we believe.
We have heard for ourselves,
and we know,
that this is indeed
the Savior of the World."

After the two days
he departed northward
into Galilee,
and came not again.
But he came to us once
and we received him,
although he performed
no miracle here,
except the changes that he worked
in the hearts of the villagers
and in me.

I have seen the Christ.
He spoke to me.
He taught me how to love.
I have forsaken sin
and am ashamed no more.
Greatest wonder of all;
the virtuous women of the town
accept and speak to me.
I cannot know

that he is the Savior of the World.
But I do know
that he is my Savior.
I am changed.
He changed me.

VI

Mother of Dogs

An account of Jesus' meeting with a Canaanite
woman, as told, with certain explanatory comments,
by Simon the Zealot, one of the Disciples.

Mother of Dogs

I am Simon,
a disciple of Jesus.
Not the big wind of that name,
the fisherman from Galilee,
but he whom they call
the Canaanite or—
    sometimes—
the Zealot.

And by Jewish terminology
I am a Canaanite.
For so they call indiscriminately
all the descendants of people
who were settled here earlier than they.
I am—although born in Galilee
and trained as a Jew—
of Phoenician descent.

*W*e Phoenicians
were a great people
for thousands of years.
As far back as records—

129

or legends—go,
we have been a maritime nation
carrying the world's commerce.
For a time, we had competition from Crete,
whose colony Philistia
lay on the plains to the west of Judah,
but for the most part were without rivals.

We did all of Egypt's shipping,
under contract.
For her Pharaoh,
two of our captains
sailed completely around
the great land mass of Africa,
of which Egypt is but a corner,
taking several years for the effort.
This was long before
Joseph was hauled out of the lionpit
and went off to Egypt
to teach them how to organize monopoly.

During Solomon's reign,
we carried all his cargoes
from the mines of Ophir.
One of our princes,
Hiram of Tyre,
sold him—

at a good profit—

130

cedars of Lebanon
to build the Temple at Jerusalem.
He also furnished the architect,
Hiram Abiff,
who planned the Temple and,
with Phoenician workmen,
taught the clumsy tribesmen
how to square their rough stones
into finished ashlars meet for building true.
Jesus must know of this tradition;
he often speaks of rejected stones.

Even the Greeks admit
that we brought them their letters
and taught them to write.
All during the great days
of old Greece,
we were treated with respect,
and our vessels were left alone.
But finally the World-Shaker,
the Immortal Alexander,
on his way to world conquest
burned our bases
and destroyed our power.
So our star was set.
When his empire dissolved,
Rome gradually picked up the pieces
and reassembled it.

*O*ne of our great colonies
was Carthage,
whose ships regularly sailed
to the tin islands
across the channel from Gaul
for metal,
and northward to the Baltic
for amber and furs.
Rome never knew how
to build a seaworthy ship
until one of our vessels
was wrecked on her coasts
and served as a model
for her engineers.
Although Rome has destroyed Carthage
and has rubbed salt in the soil
to make it a desert forever,
the Romans have never really mastered
the art of navigation.

My mother taught me
the traditions of her people
and instilled in me
a hatred of the Romans,
who totally destroyed
great and beautiful Carthage
and run the whole civilized world
for their special benefit.
I learned to love

132

the beautiful symbols
of the old faith,
the worship of the Seven Spheres
or the seven planets.
But they had not saved us,
and their worship has gone
with our lost greatness.

*A*ll the world save Judah
accepts the Roman rule.
Here, the tradition of the Messiah,
the hope of a Savior
to throw out the foreigners
and restore the Kingdom of David,
is a live and burning expectation.
Many colorful outlaws
have sprung from ancient aristocracies
now dispossessed.
Perhaps I shall be one.
I have joined the Jews
with my whole heart
and have become a Patriot,
a fanatical Pharisee,
a Zealot, who—
    like most converts—
follows the strictest practices
of his adopted faith.
I look for the Messiah,

133

and shall fight for him.
We may lose—
it is impossible for Judah to destroy the Empire—
but we should kill some Romans first,
and that will be enough for me.

With Judas Iscariot,
an educated Jew
with whom I pair well,
I joined the underground
headed by the robber chieftain
   Barabbas,
an ignorant gangster,
but an able guerrilla fighter
who ever seeks a popular messiah
to consolidate the people in revolt.

For a time,
we thought we had found him
in John the Baptizer.
Judas and I
joined his group
as underground intelligence.
John proclaimed the Day of the Lord
and spoke out against Herod;
but he spoke of another
who was coming soon,
and would not make a deal with Barabbas.

When John was put in jail,
Jesus continued his work
and obtained a great following.
Barabbas sent Judas and me
to join up with Jesus and determine
whether he is the One Expected.

*J*esus may be the Messiah—
he does some marvelous things—
but if so, perhaps not as expected.
I doubt Barabbas can control him.
His mind is set on goodness,
not on greatness,
and the kingdom he proclaims
is one of love, not force.
I'm half afraid that he is an appeaser.
But how he makes men love him!
I have few hopes—
    and fewer illusions—
but when he talks to me
I can see angels,
and I would follow him
into the jaws of death.
But will he lead us?
Judas thinks he will,
but I do not.
I think he plans some deeper, subtler plan
than national revolt against the Empire.

And if the moment comes when I must choose,
I think I'll go with him, and not Barabbas.

A short time ago,
John the Baptizer was beheaded,
and priests were sent up
from the Temple at Jerusalem
to take stock of Jesus.
Now I am orthodox
and respect the kosher rules,
although the Temple party is conservative
and opposes revolution.
Jesus is not orthodox,
but I have to admire
the spirit and resolution
with which he routed them.
When they chided him
that his disciples ate with unwashed hands,
he answered that it never is the dirt
which going in the mouth defiles a man,
but that dirt which proceedeth out of it,
and showed them clearly he had them in mind.

They summoned Herod's soldiers.
We left our homeland
to escape arrest,
proceeding northward into Syria,
a "foreign soil" that was Phoenicia.
We journeyed quietly and peacefully

thus hoping to escape undue attention
until things had a chance to settle down.
While not in disguise,
we certainly were not proclaiming who we were.

It was, therefore, a most unwelcome thing
when a Phoenician woman came to Jesus,
identified and hailed him saying, "Lord,
have mercy upon me, O Son of David.
My daughter is severely ill at home.
I know that you can save her if you will."
She was a woman of the better class,
a young and lovely matron. How she knew
the Master, we have never learned. She spoke
a usable Aramaic, interspersed
with words of basic Greek in general use.

No Jew speaks to a woman on the streets,
not even his own wife; it isn't done.
And any woman who accosts a man
upon the highway does so for one purpose.
Besides that, he was seeking to conceal
his whereabouts and his identity.
But he could see she was no common slut,
knew she had called to him as to her king,
and sensed demanding need spoke in her tone
which he was not prepared to satisfy.
Jesus made her no answer and walked on.

Now the Phoenicians grant their womenfolk
much greater freedom than their neighbor Jews,
who have identified all sex with sin
and wish their holy men all celibate.
Phoenician worship of the Planet Moon
accepts her sovereign of fertility,
Goddess of Love in guise of Ashtoreth.
And each Phoenician maiden gives to her,
upon achieving age of puberty,
her uncut hair or her virginity.
Most keep their hair. Sailors on leave ashore
are ever ardent and are generous.
Hosea's wife was probably Phoenician,
but she renewed her worship out of boredom.
He spoke too much of love, and did too little;
a prophet should not ever take a wife.

This woman was a lady, and in need,
and followed after, loudly calling him.
And his disciples came and begged him, saying,
"Do what she asks and send her, Lord, away,
for she is crying after us and will
to the whole world proclaim our presence here."
He answered,
    "I was sent only to save
    the lost sheep of the House of Israel."

We knew that he construed his ministry
as limited alone to Israel

138

and felt he was commanded so by God.
He had discussed Ezekiel with us
and how the prophet spoke the will of God
in words he felt were binding upon him:
 Son of Man, go,
 get you to the house of Israel,
 and speak with my words to them.
 For you are not sent to a people
 of foreign speech and a hard language,
 but to the house of Israel—not to many
  peoples
 of foreign speech and a hard language,
 whose words you cannot understand.
 Surely, if I sent you to such,
 they would listen to you.
 But the house of Israel will not listen to you,
 for they are not willing to listen to me;
 because all the house of Israel
 are of a hard forehead and of a stubborn heart.*

She heard what he had said, but came and knelt
before him, and in utter disregard
of dignity and of propriety,
grasped him about the knees, and simply said,
"Lord, help me." And at last he made reply,
 "It is not fair to take the children's bread
 and throw it to the dogs beneath the table."

* Ezekiel 3:4-7.

This would have crushed a woman with less
　　poise.
But she had centuries of gentle blood
behind her, and then too she recognized
his basic goodness and nobility.
But the Phoenicians are of trader stock
accustomed to quick thinking—
　　and to argument.
Her people taught their letters to the Greeks
and business to the Jews—
　　both were apt pupils.
She smiled and made reply, "Yet, Lord, the dogs
beneath the table are allowed the crumbs
which from the children's fingers downward fall.
We dogs, although not seated at the board,
are members of the household. Your coming here
in this my time of need is such a crumb,
and my wish can be granted." She had charm
and spirit of the kind that Jesus loves.
He had tried hard to go by regulations,
but her deft parry of his unkind thrust
embarrassed and disarmed him, and revealed
parochial limits of mere Jewishness.

And Jesus answered her,
　　"O woman, great is your faith. I have not
　　　found
　　in Israel its like. You hail me King
　　and call on me in faith to heal your child,

140

but my own people will accept me not.
It shall be done for you as you desire.
Your daughter will be well."

*A*nd so it was.
She sent us word that all was well at home
and offered us her hospitality.
We could not enter into foreign homes,
but thanked her, and went on. I think this trip
did much to widen the disciples' minds
and get them ready for the broader view
should they be sent to peoples he is not.

But that lies in the future, if at all,
and we seem likelier to find our end
much closer home. I don't see what we gain
by moving northward, where we are unknown.
But he is leading; I am satisfied
to follow where he leads and take what comes.

SCRIPTURE REFERENCES

Quotations from the Old Testament appearing in the text are referenced as footnotes on the pages on which they appear.

WHICH WAY TO GOD?

Ronald E. Sleeth

People are not alike, and their ways to God are not alike.

This book for laymen takes a close look at some of the many approaches to God. It demonstrates the variety of approaches seen in the Bible, indicating their strengths and weaknesses. As he looks at their present-day counterparts, Dr. Sleeth vividly shows the immense richness of Christian experience.

Which Way to God? will encourage a broadening and deepening of the reader's own religious experience and should lead to the understanding that mature religion may encompass many different aspects of faith. "The main thing is that God works in many ways. He takes us where we are. He calls us to grow in our own experience."

As the author looks at each type of approach—the intellectual, the emo-